THE MODERN BAND

BY

STANISLAO GALLO

BOOK II

SCORE EXAMPLES

FOR USE WITH THE AUTHOR'S
TREATISE ON THE BAND

FIRST YEAR SERIES
SECOND YEAR SERIES
THIRD YEAR SERIES

C. C. BIRCHARD & COMPANY
BOSTON

Made in the United States of America

5606574

General Remarks

These score examples are given as models for a complete progressive course of study on band instrumentation to be pursued with the guidance of the author's Band Treatise.

The various instruments are indicated by symbols. In the following complete list of instruments used in the Symphony Band (printed in capitals) are added, in *italics*, the substituting instruments usually found in American bands at the present time. Other substitutions which occasionally take place, especially in foreign bands, are mentioned in the Treatise(p.90). In every case, whether any substitution occurs or not, each part of the score remains unchanged.

In the Treatise several different instrumental groups are considered, including both the Symphony Band of 75 players and the Military Band of 50 players, by either of which the various examples in full score may be performed, disclosing the best characteristics of the two types of band in their completeness. See paragraphs 99 to 105 inclusive.

By applying the system of "cueing" explained in the Treatise most of the full-score examples of the series may be made adaptable for reduced bands — symphonic or military. See par. 106 et seq.

N.B. The symbols B1-2-3 and C1-2 stand for Flutes and Oboes respectively. Only when the Piccolo and the English Horn interchange on those parts, are they indicated accordingly.

SYMBOLS AND RESPECTIVE NAMES OF INSTRUMENTS

Section I

$A\frac{1}{2}$ SOPRANINO CLARINETS (in E♭)

A1   First SOPRANO CLARINETS (in B♭)

A2   Second SOPRANO CLARINETS (in B♭)

A3   ALTO CLARINETS (in E♭)
    or Alto Saxophones II - III

A4   BASS CLARINETS (in C)
    or 'Cellos

A5   CONTRABASS CLARINETS (in C)
    or String Double Basses

Section II

B1-2-3 FLUTES and PICCOLOS I-II-III

C1-2   OBOES I-II and ENGLISH HORN (ad lib.)

D1   SOPRANO SAXOPHONE
    or B♭ Clarinet (obbligato)

D2   ALTO SAXOPHONE

D3   TENOR SAXOPHONE

D4   BARITONE SAXOPHONE

E1-2   SARRUSOPHONES I-II
    or Bassoons

E3   CONTRA-SARRUSOPHONE
    or Contra-Bassoon

Section III

F1-2-3-4 E♭ HORNS I-II-III-IV

G1-2-3   B♭ TRUMPETS I-II-III
    or Cornets (2nd 3rd and 4th)

H1-2   TENOR TROMBONES I-II

H3-4   BASS TROMBONES III-IV

I1-2   SOPRANO SAXHORNS I-II
    or Cornets (Solo)

I3   MEZZO-SOPRANO SAXHORN
    or Cornet (1st)

I4   ALTO SAXHORN

I5   TENOR SAXHORN
    or Trombone (Solo)

I6   BARITONE SAXHORN
    or Euphonium

I7   BASS SAXHORN
    or E♭ (or F) Tuba

I8   CONTRABASS SAXHORN
    or BB♭ (or CC) Tuba

Section IV

J1   TIMPANI, etc.

J2   SIDE DRUM, etc.

J3   BASS DRUM, CYMBALS, etc.

Special Instruments ad lib.

K1   CELESTA

L1   HARP

SCORE EXAMPLES

FIRST YEAR SERIES

Contents
(First Year Score Examples)

CHORALS FOR SECTION I: CLARINETS

CHORALS FOR SECTION II: CONIC-WOOD

CHORALS FOR SECTION III: BRASS

FIRST YEAR SCORE EXAMPLES
CHORALS FOR SECTION I—CLARINETS
PLAIN TRANSCRIPTION OF A CHORAL FOR A1-2-3-4

The four voice parts are copied or transposed, note for note, to the four instruments.

Johann Sebastian Bach. *Gottes Sohn ist kommen*

THE FOUR VOICES IN OPEN POSITION
(See Part II, paragraph 143)

The *bass8* (indicated ⌐——⌐) will avoid the extra large "space" between the two lower parts. The two parallel fifths (+ +) resulting from inverted fourths are not objectionable in instrumental music. See Part II, paragraph 158.

Bach. *Ach Gott, erhör' mein Seufzen*

CROSSING OF PARTS
(the *soprano* to A3)

In two places the *bass* is changed to the octave above owing to the limited compass of the ordinary Bass Clarinets in C. But should these instruments possess the four extra bottom notes (see Part I, page xv) or should the part A4 be played by 'Cellos (Part I, page xxxi) the given small notes would come within the reach of either instrument.

Bach. *Du, o schönes Weltgebäude*

The original setting of voices is kept throughout.

Bach. *Nun ruhen alle Wälder*

The *soprano*[8] in $A\frac{1}{2}$ gives a light, harmonic-like effect, and the *bass*[8] in A5 adds solidity to the harmonic structure. To fill in the extra large interval, at the end of the second measure A4 enters on the *bass*[8].

5

Bach. *Ihr Gestirn', ihr hohlen Lüfte*

At (a), crossing of parts with the *soprano* to A4. This four-part arrangement is often used in orchestra with the 'Cello taking the melody. At (b), open position; A½ and A1 in unison on the *soprano*8; the *bass*8 in A5 increases the vagueness of the open position. The change to close position at (c), with octaves on the extreme voices produces a striking sonorous effect. The opposed contrast is attained at (d) where the choral ends in open position without the extreme instruments.

6

Bach. *Wenn wir in höchsten Nöten sein*

REMARK: The free parts in all these choral exercises are shown in small notes. See Part II, paragraphs 146 and 147.

The continuous free part in this choral is given alternately to A2-3-4. The *bass* is lowered an octave at the places indicate

thus: ⌐‾‾‾‾⌐

7

Bach. *Gottlob, es geht nunmehr zu Ene*

REDUCED GROUPS AND DIVISI
(See Part II, paragraph 194 et seq.)

(a) The *soprano* in octaves to A1 divisi and the other voices in open position — 8 instruments on the top part and 4 on each of the other five parts. (b) Close position for two A1 divisi (soli), one A3 and one A4. (c) A2-3, both groups divisi. (d) The entire section with A½ on the *alto* and A2 divisi on the *alto* and the free part.

8   Bach. *Von Gott will ich nicht lassen*

EVERY VOICE RAISED AN OCTAVE
(Part II, Paragraph 145)

(a) The four voices an octave higher for A1-2, both groups divisi. (b) A½ and A3 (2 soli) enter on the free part also an octave higher. (C) The choral in the original pitch for A2, A3 divisi and A4, *(2 soli)*—A5, also *2 soli*, playing the *bass₈*. (d) The octave position as at (a) is resumed, but this time by A1-2-3-4 soli.

Bach. *Erstanden ist der heil'ge Christ*

THE VOICES IN SUPERPOSED OCTAVES
(Part II, Paragraph 148)

The choral is opened an octave above its original pitch. At (a) the three upper voices become superposed octaves to the quartet which is introduced in the original pitch. (b) The period closes in a plain transcription of the four voices. (C) Here the superposed harmony is effected by the three upper voices in octaves given respectively to A1-2-3 divisi.

REMARK: Having the harmony complete in the upper parts, the original cross position between *tenor* and *bass*, indicated by +, is avoided, thus gaining in harmonic clearness.

Bach. *Mit Fried' und Freud' ich fahr' dahin*

OVERLAYED UNISONS
THE *SOPRANO* AS AN INNER PART
CROSSING OF VOICES

(a) The upper voices all doubled, including the *soprano* as an inner part. The latter is allowed only if it does not run below the *bass* and its melodic line does not create passing-note dissonances with the nearest parts. (b) Crossing of voices (Part II, paragraph 144) *i.e.* the *soprano*₈ to A3 *tutti* and the other voices in their original pitch, each one performed by two instruments only. At (c) also crossing of voices, the *soprano* is taken by A4; in this instance the *bass* too is lowered an octave. (d) Regular distribution of parts with the inner voices overlayed (*alto* in A½ and A2) and the extreme voices with octaves above and below.

Bach. *Sei Lob und Ehr' dem höchsten Gut*

SOLO QUARTET FOR SAXOPHONES

The choral opens and ends, at (C), in plain transcription. Two instances of crossing of parts occur when the *soprano* is taken, at (a) by D3, and at (b) by D2.

Bach. *Ach Gott, vom Hümmel sich darein*

THREE FLUTES AND ONE ALTO FLUTE ad lib.

NOTE: In absence of the Alto Flute its part is played, preferably, by an Alto Clarinet (major 3rd higher).

The original pitch of the choral at (a) and (C) is raised an octave in all the voices. At (b) and (d) the regular open position is effected by crossing the middle voices, the *alto* (in B3) being played in its original pitch.

Bach. *Helft mir Gott's Güte preisen*

DOUBLE-REED INSTRUMENTS

The first half of the choral is changed from close to open position, with the *bass*$_8$ in E3 at the second period only. At (a) the close position is retained with C2 (English Horn) on the *soprano* and E3 on the *bass* which is lowered an octave at the 3rd, 4th and 5th measures. At (b), E2 taking a free part, the choral ends with the entire double-reed group in close position.

14

Bach. *Wie schön leuchtet der Morgenstern*

Alternating (a) single-reed quartet, (b) double-reed quartet, (C) both single and double-reed in overlayed harmony with E3 on the *bass*₈. At (d) an effective crossing of voices is used with the *soprano*₈ in D3. See Part II, paragraph 144 at *(2)*.

15

Bach. *O Haupt Blut und Wunden*

(a) The four voices in the original pitch held by the Saxophones are superposed by the octaves of the three upper voices in the Flut
(b) The choral in open position for two Saxophones and three Flutes, two of the latter doubling on the weak Flute register.   (c) Th
extra large intervals of the open position are filled in by the entrance of D1 and D3 on the *soprano* and *tenor* respectively. (d) Th
arrangement as at (a) is reassumed.

Note the different dynamic marks in this example to attain the tonal balance between strong and weak toned instruments,   an
also between the upper and the feeble low register of the Flutes. See Part II, paragraph 170.

Bach. *Der Herr ist mein getreuer Hir*

(a) Three Flutes, two of which doubling on the *alto*, and three double-reeds. (b) Five double-reeds, soli. (C) Tutti in superposed harmony. (d) Double-reed quintet (free part for English Horn) with the first Flute on the *soprano*⁸.

17

Bach. *Nun ruhen alle Wälder*

FUSION OF TIMBRE IN SECTION II
EACH VOICE TO ONE INSTRUMENT (NO DOUBLING)

Distant-like answers in open position at (a) and (b)

Bach. *Gott hat das Evangelium*

(b)

DOUBLINGS AND SOLO PARTS
IN A CHORAL FOR SECTION II

(a) Two instruments on each voice (overlayed unison) and octaves to the extreme voices. (b) The four voices octave higher to three

Bach: *Jesu, Jesu, du bist mei*

Flutes and one Saxophone with the two periods ending in full chords. (C) Open position with three Flutes on the *soprano*^{8} and two instruments of different timbre on each of the other voices. (d) The same parts continue with the addition of D$_1$ on the *alto*^{8} and E$_1$ on the *tenor,* thus filling in the extra large intervals between the upper parts. (e) Another mellow and rich sonority of the entire section in superposed and overlayed harmony.

TRUMPETS AND TROMBONES

(a) Crossing of voices with the *soprano*₈ in H1, resulting in a male-quartet-like effect: see Part II, paragraph 144. (b) Plain transcription of the four voices with additional free parts. (c) The middle voices doubled, *pianissimo*, and the extreme voices single *mezzo-forte*. (d) The male quartet effect as at (a) is resumed, to which there is added a muted Trumpet on the *soprano*, the notes of which sound as if they were light overtones of the melody an octave below.

20

Bach: *Alle Menschen müssen sterben*

(a) Three brass quartets are presented successively: H1-2-3-4, F1-2-3-4 and G1-2 & H1-2, in every one the original voice pitch being kept. (b) The middle voices doubled by instruments of different timbre (two Horns balancing with one Trumpet or Trombone, see Part II, paragraph 170), and the extreme voices doubled by instruments of the same timbre. (C) Each voice doubled by instruments of the same group, resulting in a contrast of the three different timbres. (d) A rich and sweet fusion of the three timbres.

21   Bach: *Vater unser im Himmelreich*

(a) Solo quartet. (b) I2 and I4 enter with free parts. (C) Tutti in a sonorous fusion; here the original open harmony is filled in by I2 on a free part and by I4 on the *soprano*$_8$ for two measures and then on a second free part; the *bass*$_8$ is also added. At (d) for filling in the open chords and extending them downward (superposed harmony), the *bass* has been lowered an octave and to the three original upper voices in I1 I3 and I5 has been added the *tenor*$_8$ in I2, the *soprano*$_8$ in I4 and the *alto*$_8$ in I6.

22

Bach: *Jesu, meiner Seelen Wonne*

THE ENTIRE BRASS SECTION
IN DIFFERENT NUMERICAL STRENGTH

In this choral the four voices, kept throughout in their original pitch, are distributed to the various brass instruments as follows:

Bach: *Weg, mein Herz, mit den Gedanken*

each voice *solo* at (e); *solo*, muted at (f); doubled at (a); tripled at (b) and quadrupled at (c). In addition to the latter (the voices quadrupled), at (d) the *bass₈* is introduced by three instruments.

A FIVE-PART CHORUS FOR THE BRASS

The two canons developed in this composition — the first canon held by the *tenor* and the *bass* and the second canon (composed of fragments of the first) held by the *soprano* and the *altos I & II* — are transcribed for the brass instruments alternating at

Palestrina: *Agnus Dei*

each new entrance a different sonority, i.e., different strength, fusion of timbre, or contrast of timbre. The example is analyzed by the symbols of each instrument used, indicated over the voice parts at the first entrance and wherever a change of instrumentation occurs. This system of annotating by symbols the fragment of music to be scored will be found very helpful in planning beforehand the appropriate distribution of parts to the various instruments employed. See Part II, paragraph 141.

33

SCORE EXAMPLES

SECOND YEAR SERIES

Contents

(Second Year Score Examples)

SECOND YEAR SCORE EXAMPLES
CHORALS FOR VARIOUS ENSEMBLES

The analytic notes, as given on each example of the preceding series, are omitted here, thus to initiate the student in score-reading. He should carefully analyze the distribution of voices at each period of the Choral where the instrumentation is successively changed; thence he should employ *the same* distribution of voices in other chorals selected from the Bach collection.

The free parts are also shown here in small notes, but only in the band parts, and not also in the original as in the first year series.

25 SECTIONS I AND II

Bach: *Gott sei gelobet und gebenedeiet*

41

27. SECTIONS II and III

Bach: *Hilf, Gott, dass mir's gelinge*

44

28 SECTIONS I II and III

Bach: *Jesu, nun sei gepreis*

TRANSCRIPTION FROM THE ORCHESTRAL SCORE

The orchestral parts in this example are merely copied or transposed for the corresponding instruments of the band score (see Part II, paragraph 92). The *solo* of the 1st Clarinet could, in the band, be given to the principal Clarinet, but the Soprano Saxophone will stand out in sharper relief from the background of the Clarinet ensemble which carries the string parts. See Part II, paragraph 206 et seq.

Pizzicato passages transcribed for wind instruments are indicated "*come pizz.*" and are performed in a more or less sharp staccato, according to speed, dynamic-degree, and the style of the music.

29 - Orig. [$\frac{3}{4}$ Adagio]

Ludwig van Beethoven. *4th Symphony in B*

TRANSCRIPTION FROM THE ORCHESTRAL SCORE

29 $\begin{bmatrix} 3 \\ 4 \end{bmatrix}$ Adagio

Ludwig van Beethoven. *4th Symphony in Bb*

This is another example showing the ease of transcribing from the orchestra to this type of band score—each part, one by one, being simply copied or transposed from the respective orchestral part. Here, too, the Soprano Saxophone is most effective for th[e] original Clarinet *solo*. See the reason for the use of A-Clarinet in this case: Part II, par. 132 and foot-note.

30-Orig. [C] Moderato ♩=56

Giuseppe Martucci. *Notturn[o]*

30- [C Moderato ♩=56]

Giuseppe Martucci. *Notturno*

54

Here also the original setting is kept intact in the band transcription.

Should Bass and Contrabass Clarinets in C be used, and should they lack the extra low semitones (Part I, page xv) the low D at *(a)*, ninth measure, would be beyond their reach. But with A5 *divisi in octava* and with the aid of E1-2 the interruption of the passage will hardly be observed.

Ludwig van Beethoven. *Overture No. 3, "Leonore"*

31 [3/4 Adagio]

56

In the first half of this example the original setting is kept, excepting the first two measures of the 2nd Violins *divisi* which are given instead to both the 1st and 2nd Clarinets, six on each part.

In the last half of the example there is a careful reinforcement of the Grand Quintet by four Saxhorns. If the dynamic marks are observed the Saxhorns will add to the Clarinets' sonority, amalgamating with their tone color in an effect like that of the string ensemble.

32 Orig.   Giovanni Sgambati. *Sinfonia: Op. 16*

By permission of the original publishers, B. Schott's Söhne, Mainz.

58

As the original key would, in several places, prove too difficult for the band, the transposition down a half-tone has been chosen as the most suitable to the character of this work.   Part II, paragraph 137.

The entrance in unison of the two Clarinets has been given to D2-3 and the succeeding part of the first Clarinet to D1.

The rhythm of the two Horns, — which outdoors would be somewhat weak — is reinforced by I5-6. To these is added I7 of the *bass* part instead of dividing A4 as in the original 'Cello part.   Thus arranged, the band transcription results in a perfect tonal balance.

33- Orig.

Leone Sinigaglia. *Danze Piemontesi*
(*No. 1*)

By kind permission of Breitkopf & Härtel, Leipzig

33

The entire *Vorspiel und Isolde's Liebestod*, for band, is transcribed one tone lower both on account of the succeeding modulations in difficult sharp-keys, and of the fact that the string parts run very high in many places.

The Mezzo-Soprano Saxhorn reinforcing the Bass Clarinets adds to the solo of the 'Cellos the required strength and vitality, and also that peculiar metallic timbre of the high 'Cello *tessitura*.

Having at our disposal only one Oboe (C2 having taken the English Horn) the 2d Oboe notes are given alternately to D1 & D2.

34 – Orig.

Richard Wagner. *Tristan und Isolde*
(Vorspiel)

Lento, amoroso

Richard Wagner. *Tristan und Isolde*
(*Vorspiel*)

The fingered tremolos in this example are so distributed that each is easy on the respective instrument. See tables on trills and tremolos for keyed instruments in Part I.

A bowed tremolo of not too long duration can be given in "lip tremolo" to single-reed instruments — Clarinets and Saxophones on which it is performed with a rapid tongue-beating. But should the bowed tremolos be soft, like those in this example, the Clarinets alone should be used on the lip tremolos, indicating them *leggiero*.

Tremolo passages of A4-5 are written sustained when these parts are cued for the low Saxhorns. See Part II, paragraphs 97 and 101.

35- Orig.

Arrigo Boito. *Mefistofele*

35

Arrigo Boito. *Mefistofele*

64

Owing to the importance of the two Piccolos in the last measure, their parts are assigned to B1-2. The Flute solo in B3 may, for reduced band, be *cued* in A ½.

The only additions to the original setting are the two Saxhorns (I5-6) reinforcing the bottom fifth of the chord at *crescendo*

The first entrance of the Bass Clarinet (orig.) is given to D4 and the second entrance to D3. These two instruments, together with D2, toward the end of the *crescendo* gradually combine on the sustained chord in open position.

36 – Orig.

Leo Sowerby. *Money Musk*

Leo Sowerby. *Money Musk*

66

The beautiful, ethereal effect of the Strings *con sordine* being itself inimitable, at least its degree of sonority can be reprodu-
ced with the Clarinets, which can reduce their tone to a *velato* (veiled quality) resembling far-off, distant sounds.When the String
con sordine are indicated *pp* or *ppp* the Clarinets are reduced in number accordingly and marked *velato*.

For out-door performance the harmonics of the Harp are changed to natural tones.

REMARK. To perform competently music of this type the *large* band is required. Although it might be possible to reduce it fo
a *medium* band, for smaller combinations the attempt would be futile.

Ottorino Respighi   *Ballata delle Gnomid*

37–Orig.

By kind permission of *G.Ricordi & C. Milano*

Ottorino Respighi. *Ballata delle Gnomidi*

SCORE EXAMPLES

THIRD YEAR SERIES

Contents
(Third Year Score Examples)

TRANSCRIPTION FROM ORCHESTRA AND VOICES

INSTRUMENTATION FROM THE ORGAN

INSTRUMENTATION FROM THE PIANO

WORKS ORIGINALLY SCORED FOR SYMPHONY BAND

THIRD YEAR SCORE EXAMPLES

TRANSCRIPTION FROM ORCHESTRA AND VOICES

In the band transcription of this number the "chorus effect" is suggested by the use of six Saxhorns; two each playing, *piano*, the *soprano* and *tenor,* and one each playing, *mezzo-forte*, the *alto* and *bass.* See Part II, paragraph 236.

When vocal parts are transcribed for instruments,"extra syllable"notes are omitted. See Part II, paragraph 178.

In the transcription a number of the more delicate parts are doubled to attain a better balance in open-air performance. viz., the low octave of the Flutes in the 3rd and 4th measures is doubled by D2; the first entrance of the Bassoon is played *a 2;* and the two Bassoons in octaves (last measure) are doubled by D3-4. The two Horn parts are also doubled.

38- Orig. [4/4 - Moderato e solenne ♩=54]   Edward Elgar. *The dream of Gerontius*

38 [4/4 - Moderato e solenne ♩=54]

Edward Elgar. *The dream of Gerontius*

In this example each part of the chorus is given to three brass instruments (G, H & I). D3-4 replace the original 1st pair of Bassoons. A ½ (solo) *ppp* reinforces the 2nd Flute at (*a*) and the 3rd Flute at (*b*).

39– Orig. [**c**-Andante ♩=84]

Giuseppe Verdi   *Messa da Requiem (Agnus Dei*

39 [C- Andante ♩=84]   Giuseppe Verdi *Messa da Requiem (Agnus Dei)*

In this example the combination of two muted Saxhorns *p* and two Saxophones *pp* seems to be the best choice for the parts of voices *a bocca chiusa* (with closed mouth) behind the scene.

The Viola d'Amore is here used merely to maintain the intonation of the chorus, not to be audible to the audience, thus its part is not represented in the band transcription.

The last chord of the full Violin section *con sordine* is distributed to 8 Clarinets — two for each note — *ppp*, *velato*. The 1st Oboe on the lowest note of the Violins (B♭) accentuates the effect of distant sounds dying out in the night.

40-Orig.

Giacomo Puccini. *Madama Butterfly*

By kind permission of G. Ricordi & Co. Milano

The four principal voice parts in this example are transcribed for G1-2-3 and H1, and the chorus parts for I1 to 6. The upper octave of the 1st Violins is held by B1-2-3 and A½. On the fifth measure of the latter (A½) the upper octave in parenthesis is used only if the performers are expert in that extreme register. In high passages, such as this, the use of the A♭ Sopranino Clarinet would be desirable.

The slow tremolos of the 2nd Violins and Violas are rearranged for A2-3 in their easiest fingering positions according to the table in Part I, p. 46. At the seventh measure the tremolos in D2-3, which are also easy, see table p. 53, Part I, are added to improve the harmonic balance.

41- Orig. [3/4 - Allegro molto e sostenuto ♩. = 60]

George W. Chadwick. Noë

By kind permission of the Composer.

41 [3/4 - Allegro molto e sostenuto ♩.= 60]

George W. Chadwick. *Noël*

The author uses no signatures in this work, the required accidentals being placed before the notes. This is a very usual procedure in music of vague, unsettled tonality, and is of course, followed in the band score. Enharmonic changes occur frequently in this type of music. Here a change from F# to G♭ is effected in the fourth measure.

The entrance *p* of the chorus is given to brass instruments, all of mellow tone, namely two Saxhorns for each extreme voice and one Saxhorn and two Horns for each middle voice, giving a soft, sweet timbre. At the *ff* the vocal parts are also held by the brass, but are treated more in instrumental style, viz: the first entrance being assigned to 3 Saxhorns, the second to 3 Trumpets, the third to 4 Horns and the fourth to 3 Trombones, thus the various timbres of the Brass coming out in contrast with each other.

At the fourth measure D3 takes the original 3rd Horn part and D4 reinforces E2. In the same measure I5-6 join A4 on the bass^8.

42 – Orig. [$\frac{2}{4}$($\frac{6}{8}$) Allegretto]

G. Francesco Malipiero. *La Principessa Ulalia*

42 $\left[\frac{2}{4}\left(\frac{6}{8}\right) \text{ Allegretto}\right]$

G. Francesco Malipiero. *La Principessa Ulalia*

INSTRUMENTATION FROM THE ORGAN

Remark: Information on the Organ regarding notation, actual sound of the various pipes, stops and keyboards, given in Part I.

Alfred Hollins. *Grand Choeu*

43 [3/4 Tempo di Minuetto, pomposo]

44 [**c** Allegretto]

W. Wolstenholme. *Lied*

45. $\left[\begin{smallmatrix}2\\4\end{smallmatrix}\right.$ – Allegro vivace $\left.\right]$

Pietro A. Yon. *Rapsodia Italiana*

46. [**c** - Quasi allegro]

César Franck. *Trois Chorals* (№ 3)

The exact reproduction of the original *tessitura* is kept throughout the example which, in its simplicity, discloses several tonal combinations of effective and easy execution.

47 Moderato, un pò maestoso

Ferruccio Busoni. *Elegien* (No. 3)

The instrumentation of this piece in the key of *e-minor* is both beautiful and easy. Movements such as this —of simple structure and slow tempo—even with 2,3,or 4 sharps are practicable and very effective for band. See part II, paragraph 131.

48.

Alexander Scriabin: *Prelude*

Note the sustained *bass in fifths* suggested by the *Ped.* At (a) two Flutes, an octave above the original *tessitura* of the two upper parts, add brilliancy to the passage. At (b) the Triangle marks the light rhythm of the descending sequence.

49. [3/8 – Allegro scherzando]

Cyril Scott. *Inclination à la Danse*

In this example is shown a careful distribution of a complex harmonic structure. See Part II, paragraph 152. Harmonic change occur in various places. In music of this nature—of uncertain tonality, or absolutely atonal (Part II, paragraph 151 and illustrati [c]) — no key signature is given to the band parts, the required accidentals being placed before each note.

N.B. A reduction of this full band score is possible, but for *medium band* only.

50

The original pitch and *tessitura* of parts are retained in this example. Its key, however, has been changed throughout enharmonically from sharps to flats. See Part II, paragraph 134 and subsequent chart on keys.

By kind permission of *G. Ricordi & C., Milano.*

52

Lento, stanco (♩ = 52 a 66)

Ildebrando Pizzetti da Parma
Da un autunno già lontano (No.

WORKS ORIGINALLY SCORED FOR SYMPHONY BAND

53

Henry F. Gilbert: *Pilgrim Tercentenary Pagea*
(Plymouth, Mass. 1921)

55

Stanislao Gallo. *Tarantella at Piedigrotta*
(Three Neapolitan Sketches – No.3

The first half of this example illustrates a lightly scored passage with *cues* for reduced band, and the last half a *tutti* in which the various parts are distributed in such a manner as to afford completeness and balance should the score be used by a *medium* or a *small* band, symphonic or military. See Part II, paragraphs 110, 111 and 112.

Stanislao Gallo. *After the Victory (Symphonic Poem)*